A LITTLE
VILLAGE GIRL

A Book of Short Stories

Vol. 1

By
Melissa Jadoonanan

EBOOK ISBN: 978-969-2592-51-2

PAPERBACK ISBN: 978-969-2592-52-9

HARDBACK ISBN: 978-969-2592-53-6

Dedication

For my children, Shaila & Paavan

Contents

The Meeting

⸻❧⸻

Finally, she had asked him to come over after weeks of pussy-footing. Now there would be no screen to safely hide behind. No 'semicolon-ing', no 'apostrophe-ing', no deleting, just him and whatever words she might have been able to squeeze through. The sound of the voice on the other end of the line made her stop. This moment felt like a lifetime in the making.

She didn't need a sixth sense to know the butterflies in her stomach felt like pigeons. "I think I'm in front of your house!" She knew he was coming but they hadn't set a time. Just how she preferred the madness, unscheduled. "Be down in a sec…" I managed the words.

The scathing looks that shot from her eyes on taking a last look at the mountain of clothes lying lifelessly on the bed agitated her. One coffee meeting was not supposed to turn her room upside down, but it did. She closed the door behind her and proceeded downstairs. Thank God, we can closet ourselves, close doors, cover things to ensure we don't appear as if we spill out. How utterly human and unacceptable that would be if people knew we were not always put together neatly like little ceramic ornaments sitting, uselessly, but poignantly perfect.

This friend request was different. I didn't know what awaited me when I selected the "add friend" option, Ritesh Singh. His ice breaker was award winning. But then again, how could flattery fail. He had stated in his first line to me and seemed genuinely rather confused, that he thought he was messaging Deepika Padukone. I, quite absentmindedly replied, "Are you messaging the wrong person?" He said, "No, do you know who she is?" Apparently, she is big Bollywood news. I was feeling quite pleased; that's how the award went to Ritesh. And that wasn't even why he qualified to get my time and steal my thoughts. It turned out I remembered who he was. I used to gape at him in temple. But not too much, as his arm was heavily ornamented with his very stunning girlfriend who graduated to be his wife and thence his ex-wife.

Short story about my life in a nutshell. It's no different than most of ours. I had a past, it was over, this is my present. The trick about telling that story is we keep repeating the past in the present. So, the moment of the present is sullied by the hues of

2

the past. Very messy business. With that pattern, no one hopes to welcome a future that resembles the massacre at Tiananmen Square. A harbinger of harsh realities, much? Leave the past in the past. Let it pass. "This too, shall pass." Somebody said that...ah my old friend, Jesus!

Anyway, apparently someone whom I had entrusted my thoughts to about how gorgeous he was didn't quite grasp the concept of what confidentiality meant and what flowed from that mis-snake was that all I could have done was literally steal glimpses of him at temple. I had to hope the sun was orbiting the earth right at that moment when I looked up. That's a tricky thing to navigate. Who knew which planet I might have not appeased, or which lesson I had not yet learnt and was again repeating itself all for my benefit!

He didn't even know I existed back then, some odd ten years or so ago. Because I couldn't offend the planets any more than I had or hoped that my six Saturdays could somehow be close enough to the required nine for salvation, I had to take my own chances. Even the lord of the skies shook his head in absolute derision of my choices. But Lord Hanuman had my back. It was a Saturday evening; I had registered for Hanuman pooja and was idly walking around the 85 ft. majestic Lord Hanuman statue, inaugurated by Swamiji.

To the world, Swamiji is known as Sri Sri Ganapathy Sachchidanada, Pontiff of the Datta Treya Yoga Centre in Carapichima Trinidad. For us however, Appaji was the name to refer to our revered, loving, gracious, and funny teacher, Swamiji.

I was trying to remember the direction of the yantra (the sacred geometry), the prescribed way one is meant to walk around the eighty-five feet statue of Hanumanji so as to get the maximum benefit of creating new pathways in your mind and simultaneously repeat the mantra while walking. It was not for beginners like me. Little children, whose parents knew these routines, did it effortlessly, almost without thinking. How could they not, they learnt it in utero. I felt like a complete idiot because I always felt like I didn't know how to pray. I didn't know how to belong. I would always, in the middle of the mantra, start apologizing to Hanumanji for the mistakes. I would also plead with him to forgive my less than gracious steps. It almost always ended up in a conversation, with me doing all the talking; sometimes in my head.

Ritesh was making his revolution through the inner doorways and outer doorways of the yantra, like a boss! I looked on enviably at first, at the ease at which some could perform tasks. That kind of ease seemed enviable. With that obstacle out of the way, one can really get a head start on the business at hand. Start the communion of prana and prakti. See how the two became one. Tat tvam asi (thou are that). But those lofty aspirations were for the deserving ones. The aspirants who took their children to Krishna Kirtan, and who were schooled on mediating from two years old.

The ones who treated pranayama like the gift it was. Food for thought. The ones who performed the austere rigid religious practices designed to help control the monkey mind and the rouge senses. I wondered if King Dhrtarastra knew his entire purpose was to teach that a kingdom ruled by a king, who was ruled by his senses, was to have a blind sense king, and therefore be resolved to be blind, spiritually? Anyway, it wasn't my business whether King Dhrtarastra lived his purpose or not.

The most I had done on spirituality was read a book on kundalini and attempted to practice without the help of a teacher, which ended in disaster. Maybe I could blame unleashing kundalini as one of the reasons for the irreconcilable differences. They should have had a warning. Wait, they did, as per everything under the sun, that I felt couldn't pertain to me.

I was indestructible; irreverent; and I bent the rules of the world to my individual constitution. I did not consider myself a rebel. I wasn't. I was just different. How can some sounds, called seed mantras, open gateways in a spiritual body, so much to cause an upheaval in the physical body? It can, it did, cause a manifestation of unreasonable behavior.

Ritesh's girlfriend adorned her arm with his while making their way to Hanumanji. They had registered for pooja as well. So, I hurried myself along the walkway, as if I hadn't even noticed him. I had. I begged Lord Hanuman, please let him see me if only this once, in this glimpse, for a nano second of a look, let his eyes meet mine. I didn't know what petitions Lord Hanuman had to make or what mitigations he entered into on my behalf. Just at that moment, as I averted my gaze to adjust my sari shawl over my right shoulder, I found his stare. Between a handful of hair he was coaxing to stay back and out of his eyes. I lifted my eyes just beneath my eyelashes, endeavoring to not make that eye contact which I prayed for.

Thank you Hanumanji. I quickly dismissed the happenstance and vowed to do the nine Saturdays with no shortcuts!

Ten years later, a divorce of my own and two children, I sat chatting nonchalantly with Ritesh over the unscheduled cup of coffee about our children's names, the past, the fun in finding out what we thought of each other back then. Did he really notice me, or was that my imagination? And of course, flattery mixed with sincerity, earned him a second meeting.

A Village Girl Falls Apart_

⌁⌁

Nineteenth February, 2019. Today is the first day I am home alone since mom passed. What a stupid looking date, (19/02/19) My other self would exclaim, "synchronicity!" and become unraveled and wrapped up in the sheer occurrence of the date. This version of me today couldn't care the fuck less! Five weeks ago, we welcomed her home. I saw the 'deathness' that greeted me.

It irreverently waved its stench in my face. But I ignored it. How dare it! To even become distracted by its presence would have been an insult to her intention for being here; rest, relaxation, re-charge! In sweet, sweet T&T, oh how she loves up her country.

Humph! If death simply needs me to acknowledge its macabre attire, I would have, had I known its wrath is real. I always loved writing with pencils, but I forgot how much one's hand can cramp up. Thanks to Shaila, I have an array of alternatives. Today she heard me use a word and instinctively, like wet is to

9

water, popped up and said, "What does that word mean, Mommy?"

She is the daughter I never thought I was worthy to have. How could I? I never thought I was qualified to earn a daughter who was so many things all rolled up in one and who could be approved to be mine. I still ask myself, what was this system of selection, this process obviously flawed in its mechanics of arriving at me as "final output." So, while I await a call back from the "selectors" I am using this opportunity disguised as her mom to learn as much as I can from her.

I smile when I find the memory of her; her everythingness makes me feel like somewhere, on this strange rock of existence, all the world is right; well at least mine!

A deep sigh brings me back to myself. 19/02/19. Stupid synchronicity. How could anything positive have been heralded by these events that rocked our world.

I have always been an idiot. A special kind of ass. Always pushing. Fencing. Running. I thought I had properly cordoned myself off from events such as this one. God knows, I have been perfecting the art since age seven. How wrong! So wrong! Can't even do that right! Distance myself enough so as to not be affected! Where does my internal mechanism of "how to do things" come from, "made in China; no offense to the world's manufacturer!

The noise from the neighbor's electric tile cutter breaks my gaze and I remember, she is dead. Dead. She died. Because I didn't heed death's notice. "Ignore it!" I said. "Feed her!" I said. "Or she would die!" I said. "If you don't eat, you will die!" were my last words to her. "It's ok," we're hers. I did acknowledge it, but quickly dismissed it because I was too blinded by my own ego.

Couldn't see her like that. So, didn't. What a fool. Quickly took out my protective blanket and shielded myself from what my poor little self could not bear to witness. I should be in the daughter's reject pile. But wait! They might take Shaila back! So, while this self-loathing seems appropriate and equally balanced with a healthy dose of failure in arriving at my sum total, I cannot chance doing that, at the detriment of losing the only evidence of goodness and all that is good and beautiful in my world, my daughter Shaila.

I better start looking at the thing in a different gaze or like a pregnant anorexic, eat carrots, so after the binging when you start seeing orange, it's time to stop. Must protect the growing embryo. See, there is some balance! How am I so defunct? I am the product of love. The matriarchal setup was headed by my aunt, fondly referred to as the iron lady, and my mom and my three sisters. All I have ever been surrounded by was love, comfort, support, care, and healthy attention. Wait. No. Because they didn't want our egos to burgeon and create unrealistic ideas of ourselves, they bordered on berating us. It was for our own good. "You pretty?" "I don't know what people see in you nah?" Up to today a compliment is so difficult to process. I want to ask my observer: "Are you drunk? Blind? From around here?"

Crippling love, stifling love. Love that feared I may not have survived this world. Smothering love. The love that made mothers' threats to kill children seems like a rite of passage. "I will kill you!" and on quick reflection, "with love!" So, if a child didn't want to get smothered to death, he, or she, better clean that room! She was so little, only seven they said. And standing tall, 5 ft. 3 inches at a ripe 41, they still refused to see that I had grown, if even from three feet. To this day, finding Daddy in between the hoist of his brand-new truck, crushed, remains

12

unprocessed. I am reminded of my life's to do list: "become an author"; "feel good enough"; "raise future leaders"; "feel like I belong." Already tall orders!

I wonder if it's too early for a Guinness. I mean it's lunch time somewhere on this strange rock, third from the sun! But the dizziness on getting up suggests maybe later. If I could be as focused as my American Bully, Turk, in relentless pursuit of lizards; hotdogs; donuts and bacon! Now that is an example of confidence and focus. No sign of overthinking. Just surgical execution. See iguana, catch iguana, kill iguana. Bring for Mommy. What a good dog. A loving little killer of iguanas and of all things that crawl.

The Speaker for the Nearly Dead

⌒〜⌒

With the smell of butter lingering on her fingertips from breakfast, she was unphased by the now slippery keys as she banged her keyboard in contemptuous satisfaction from both the sound and the shape of what was happening in and around her. Something seemed to be growing. A realization of sorts, where she pushed through the emotions to gain insight at a deeper level. She had to be patient with herself. But she had had enough of waiting.

Waiting seemed to be the breath that knitted this quilt of suffering she lay on at night, alone. Sometimes she felt as if that was what she ordained. Other times she was surer of the exact opposite. Why did life insist on spitting her out, every time? No matter what!

But she was that fucking resilient spirit who just wouldn't die. Her determination to learn in the various ways of "how to life" and her quest for discovering newness were the tenets of her way of life. She did things obstinately, her way. There was no religion to order her steps. No authority figure to mandate

15

results; no father, no husband, no brother. Her quorum on inception was a fistful of the most powerful women she would ever need. Like the pillars of a good society, they were her democracy and even when she tried to overthrow them, they stood immovable, like Mount Kailash! Har Har Mahadev.

Her in-born desire to turn life on its head was her only mandate, ordained by herself!

She fought and battled with unlikely opponents. She was David and Goliath! Her strength for fighting didn't come from muscles. No one knew where this scrawny little Indian girl mustered up this courage to accomplish feats not bought with money. The gangsters she worked for learnt how to respect her. And when one fell dead, shot three times in the head, all opposition ceased; all investigations eased.

But why all the fighting? Why wasn't she just a good, obedient little Indian girl? That is how they were bred. To walk behind, avert eye contact, reduce the self to that which barely resembles a shell of existence. Wait, that's what she was, as a wife, and that got her in the ring with divorce; self-destruction; self-doubt; repossessed assets, including her mind. She descended into the arena of submission. She submerged herself in defeat and failure; resigned that she was her experience of a failed marriage and therefore a failure. And with this defeatist attitude, she trudged along in life, barely seeking out a life worthy of living. She learnt how to suffer in comfort. In fact, she had become a master of the trait.

But that same submission that got her bruised and battered showed her that submission was not the superpower one employs when one wanted to conquer. Oh, how above everything else, she desired to conquer! Conquer what?! The world? Stupid little girl. So, she kicked submission into oblivion, until she needed it again to tap into its reservoirs. Submission was tricky to navigate.

She continued to stumble along all life's wrong paths! For the paths that didn't light up, she become the light and found her way out of the darkness. Cut and bleeding, she would not give up. But what was she so intent on finding? Was the reward so great?

To constantly be poised for battle required tireless revision of the skills of the art of war and juxtaposed against her new mantra, "trust in the process of life", she was conflicted. It was only after years of the same patterns of decisions she realized she wasn't fighting the world - she was fighting herself - her greatest enemy. She denied herself even the lowest level of needs. It made sense now; the quilt of loneliness was handstitched ensuring she never let love in. If it seeped in, she was sure to rip the stich, destroy the embroider, cut it out, compromising the whole. This quilt was specific to meeting the needs of her inner turmoil. Maslow would love to study this subject. She lived a life trying to prove him wrong! Why?

If one was inclined to travel the spiritual journey, submission had its place. A different kind, born from unconditional love and humility. That's a different story from this one. Self-depreciation and submission certainly had a place. It earned you entrance to fit in and, since she never belonged and was fighting to belong, she joined the queue to start to belong.

They tried to rein her in, but rules, rules, rules. In like manner, her inner programming couldn't allow it. She went against the grain. Grace, they say, is when you have exhausted your merit, but still experience divine intervention. All she had was grace. She would realize long after that even to belong she didn't care either anymore. She fought that need too. Maslow's hierarchy of needs seemed penetrable. But she learnt how to dance alone, from the seeds sown.

Her life's work caused her to meet with and mingle at a different level with kindred spirits, Paramahansa Yogananda and Jesus_Swamiji,Sai Baba, Abraham, Lord Krishna. She felt at home in their company. She didn't have to be anything. She didn't even have to be polite. What came from that was a settling in her soul. Comfort. She downed her tools and weapons and took relief. That is where she realized her spirit was replenished in the temple of her own company.

In the real world, this material world, she felt tortured. Torn. She was too material for the spiritual world, and too spiritual for the material world. A perfect conundrum that kept her at odds with herself. Apparently, she only felt whole when broken and shattered. For shit sure this qualified as self-loathing. I saw it now, as I was outside looking in.

That inner turmoil she raged against threatened to destroy her. She was reticent about these affairs of the mind. She tried to silent that mind by employing an unorthodox method of torture. Do without; stifle the need; snuff it out. You see, she was given everything in abundance, love, support — so much that somewhere in her mind she felt guilty for having received these bountifully. It felt to her as unmerited. The weight of unmerited reward she carried like a noose around her neck, shackled by guilt. She re-played that mantra she grew up hearing that tortured her existence, "To whom much is given; much is expected." She didn't amount to much in the material world, and that unmet expectation manifested as holes in her stomach.

Pain manifests in the body when one feels overwhelmed. To balance the scales of injustice and to mop up some of that excess privilege she received, like a good education, she pinched herself off success. She thought of herself as a failure, so therefore failure is what she should have been resigned to meet with. How dare she receive the privileged education and fail at marriage! She had to make an adjustment! What was the punishment for failure? - Lack of the fruits of success. So, she suffered pain for the guilt she carried for being a success and a failure. Perhaps these findings should be reported to a therapist;

to the police even. It was criminal to process thoughts like this. Is this what was considered crimes against humanity?

She felt guilty for her privilege and even more guilty to have squandered her privilege on a failed marriage.

Humans are so strange in their in-built processes.

And, to ensure she remained in that perpetual state of painful existence, she cordoned off herself from life and resolved that she would never have any of its pleasures while crying herself to sleep on her bed of nails, under her quilt of pain and punishment, in anguish as to why she felt so alone. She didn't know why.

So, she designed a life with all those achievements: education, status, notoriety. She also factored a healthy dose of "no reward for work", because of the failed marriage. This was to keep herself in check and to ensure the scales of material pleasures were evenly balanced with dissatisfaction and torture.

This equation was also applied to her personal affairs. The result of which meant only assholes walked through her door. Remember, love was not allowed in! So what kept coming through were selfish, self-absorbed assholes, who could not love others; far less love themselves. They writhed in self-torture and met others with that cold blade of discontentment. And so, she reconciled it as if this was what she attracted, this was what she was deserving of. Nothing. And not deserving of love. This seemed to balance on the scale.

But I wanted to tell her, if she would hear me- if I could slip though her impenetrable walls of insulation, was that she need not feel guilty for her life. That if she were to decide to plot the coordinates for an enjoyable life, she would not be seen as weak and/or vulnerable. That love was an energy that came from great strength, and yes, while she loved from afar, she was deserving of being loved. And yes, I knew she knew divine love, but there were other types of love she was desirous of experiencing. So, experience them and leave out the attachment to the experience. To be smart in navigating this material plain. To be where you are. You cannot deny that.

Stop trying to die. You will eventually. Please live. This land is for the living. Where is Bramha not? So, what are you searching for? Stop killing yourself. You will merge eventually.

You are here for a short time, give that ego to a higher power who can help carry it. It has burdened you for too long. Offer that ego which comes in the form of guilt, to the sacrificial fire of life! Chant the mantra that you are well deserved and deserving.

Allan Watts talks of "The Wake." He says the wake is simply that, a trail the boat leaves behind. Does the wake guide the boat? "NO!" What guides the boat is "the present moment thoughts!" Is it possible for the wake to lead the boat? "NO!" Preposterous! So, if it is as preposterous as in the analogy of Allan Watts's Wake, why isn't it readily seen in our own Wakes?

She has suffered a failed marriage. But are all relationships with the ex-husband? No! So why taint all possible relationships with the ghost of the ex-husband? So why had she been limiting her capacity for a fuller, more wholesome experience with relationships?

He explained that we can't keep using the trail to justify why we can't go where we want to go.

Where you want to go depends on your thought processes, not your trail!

To assign the guilt of a failed marriage to all round failure in life is foolish! Now that I saw it in black and white, I was not my experience of failure. In fact, that was the only example I had of failure. I was a success. I have been a success and I will continue to be a success! My wrong assessment of the experience led to my misguided notion in a belief of pain and punishment for failure; self-imposed of course.

So powerful was that disappointment of expectation from marriage that it stunted the other beliefs I held. The thoughts I forgot to keep thinking, the power of the thought! The power to transform, from the power of focus.

Mental health instability hides itself in various compartments. Get help. Talk to someone, even yourself. This is how this story all started.

If there was no more guilt, there was no more pain. If no more pain, there was a chance to experience freedom and joy on a material level.

I gave myself permission on account of my love of self, to unlock the shackles!

My Uncle Barry had a Stroke

The health system in this little Republic is home to health care anarchy. Sadly, the inhabitants expect nothing less. So, with that kind of balancing ratios, no sector was minded to strive for more.

The balance of convenience stood in perfect resistance to each other. So, when my uncle had a stroke and we had to engage the public health care system, I told my uncle to put on his bullet proof vest for the rounds of Russian roulette that were about to ensue.

Emergencies were dealt with first via the post system. If you were still alive, after the ordeal that greeted you first, from the interlude with the ambulance and thence at the local emergency clinics, a thing had to be said about "survival of the fittest." I suspected Charles Darwin might have expected his theory to look exactly like the health care system in Trinidad & Tobago. No 'meds' to minimize the deficits after the medical staff had proper reasons to suspect a stroke, obvious symptoms and all!

My uncle failed the initial evaluation. The doctor asked, "Can you lift your left leg?"

"Yes," replied my uncle and promptly lifted his right leg. The doctor chimed again, "Can you lift your left arm?" "Yes," replied my uncle and confidently lifted his right arm.

It didn't matter that the speech was slurred, and he was drooling into a little puddle just at the nape of his neck. "We can't administer any meds until we know exactly what caused the stroke, a bleed or a clot, but he is resting comfortably." So, he can die comfortably(?), I reckoned quietly. Forgetting the system I was up against, it was off to Mt. Hope Hospital. No, not the patient. He had to stay back and wait until the ambulance had enough passengers to make the trip. This was round three in the battle against death. My aunt, better referred to as 'the iron lady' and standing proudly at 75 years old, started the journey with me to Mt. Hope Hospital; we could only hope that Barry made it too.

Well, at least we didn't have to engage in the treatment plan of the village healer, Lochan. Lochan was the most available health care provider in all of Piarco, St. Helena, and Kelly Village. He would go around house to house, giving his opinion, diagnosis, and a concoction of when to take what and for how long.

Word travelled fast as to his ways in 'medicine.' Truth be told, we hadn't seen much of Lochan since they had to amputate his second leg. And, well he couldn't see much, with him losing his eyesight to vinegar and salt wash which he religiously did twice a day for a week for a self-diagnosed and self-medicated high cholesterol condition.

I wondered if anyone suggested to Lochan that vinegar and salt worked better in salads, and he stood a better chance if the formula was on lettuce and taken orally? He didn't believe in institutionalized medical care. He was an advocate for home remedying. But when we saw him at the clinic at Mt. Hope, being pushed by his wife in the wheelchair he now availed himself to, I had a sinking feeling he was losing too many body parts to his self-care.

I wondered what must have been going on for Lochan to subject himself to Mt. Hope and over the counter drugs. Perhaps it might have been the years of pig farming. Pig farming does not necessarily equate to illness, but when Lochan literally lost his house to the pigs, he had no choice but to room with them under the same roof; such scenarios can negatively impact one's health. Undesirable things. The villagers naturally assumed that Lochan contracted leptospirosis, as pigs and rats had an intimate kind of affair.

It was not until Lochan survived the ordeal and became afflicted for a second time that his son corrected the villagers and announced that Lochan was at Mt. Hope hoping to get some Panadol. He had cut his hand peeling potatoes. He was nobody's fool, and not about to pay for Panadol, when the healthcare system was giving it for free. He only went for the Panadol, for he said you could leave there with more than you went in with. He handled his own chronic illnesses. He was down to two limbs, and the ability to touch. The pigs took care of his other senses.

Anyway, his children didn't quite escape the brief interlude with the pigs as luckily as he had. One villager, better known as 'Crazy Geeta' as there were two; no, not crazies; there were far more than two. I once overheard Crazy Geeta telling my aunt a story of when she went to Lochan's parlor and meat shop to buy a beer; of course, a parlor sold beer sans license! Crazy Geeta said she saw with her own two eyes Lochan's youngest daughter Anne, wringing out the head of their parrot and putting it in the freezer. When Anne asked Crazy Geeta what she wanted, Geeta said, "Two cold parrost to go!"

Anyway, he did it his way. The pigs, the vinegar, the mental illness, it was amazing that the ones who got out of the parlor, didn't display any traits where one might have readily assumed you lived with pigs or were pig-like in any manner. Well, except for Anne, who was kind of hoggish in the way she dealt that parrot!

Musings from Mt. Hope

❦

You could be having a heart attack, hunger attack, asthma attack it don't matter; you will die at Mt. Hope. The anthem 'take a number and have a seat,' the precursor to the end.

My uncle and I dutifully joined many irrelevant lines and were greeted by many irreverent administrators. Some dispensing with the usual pleasantries and heading straight to "pee in dis!"

If by chance you silently survived your ordeal, the mask policy with the advent of Covid 19 restrictions ensured you only squeezed your way through, only missing death by a collapse and blow to the head from lack of oxygen. You 'goh' survive a buss head.

We returned the pee to the designated counter and waited in the waiting room that felt like a morgue. Only the morgue was two buildings down. I supposed energy does travel; dead or alive. But the damn Wi-Fi signal was dead like a fucking nit.

31

It only had one available seat on the return from the 'pee in dis' episode, so I opted to go outside, "thank you Jesus"! Sweet air awaited me with a Jehovah witness who was reading a magazine; I wondered if the thought was originally mine.

I stumbled into some chairs near the 'dental clinic' and paused. I didn't know if I escaped death. Cause I was still reeling from the ill effects of a lot of things.

One thing for sure; I was sure, I was not sure why, the inverse was true - I wasn't sure that I was sure why. The same damn symptoms: inability for air to reach the lungs; pain in my neck; pain all over my body; body feeling broken and splintered; hollow feeling in chest; life energy leaking out; eyes that could not keep themselves open; choking in throat; weak; faintish; feeling like my insides were crashing.

How on God's green earth was I going to describe these feelings to a doctor? They weren't even symptoms of anything. A thing if diagnosed, would have symptoms. Nobody diagnosed me.

Nuts man just passed selling cold drinks and nuts... salt and fresh! I think that was a thing indigenous to the health care system in Trini - the availability of nuts... salt and fresh. Maybe they were looking out for the stroke victims who still required a 'lil dose ah nuts an ah lil salt', whilst on their renal appointment, like my uncle.

I remained undiagnosed. So, what I could say about what I felt, remains just that. A feeling and description of the undiagnosed. But it bad. Some days, worse than others.

Anyway, I could not approach any doctor, because as it stood, I had no symptoms. Because I had nothing. I was still not sure. But I was sure this is not how anybody feels on any basis. It eh right, in fact it real wrong.

It felt real bad. I could well imagine a doctor asking me: "Yuh have pain?"

Me: "Yea."

Doctor: "Where?"

Me: "I eh sure."

Doctor: "It bad?"

Me: "Real bad."

-Doctor writes a prescription for a week supply of Panadol, the wonder over the counter drug in Trinidad.-

Me: "When to come back?"

Doctor: "If yuh still have pain."

Allyuh understand why I cyah goh by no doctor. Grief has no cure. Time, at best. So, I waited, in the waiting room, until my name was called.

Ah, a lady stopped and asked me for directions!! People really did put their hope and trust in other people, just so, just so.

I did have to see which one of my index fingers and thumbs could make an 'L'; to find where right was, and if yuh hear mih ... "two corridors down, then turn left, there you will find the main lobby!"

I didn't even know that was what it was called. The Main Lobby; papayoooo!

The people not mad yuh know. David Rudder said it the best, "we mad, we mad, we more than mad!" Is all ah we in this state of madness. "...St. Ann's!"

Is how all the patients come together in the waiting room and each become a dietitian and health expert on the do's and dont's of dietary needs when living with renal failure, or close to it.

I had never heard my uncle so vocal and confident as he metamorphosed in the waiting room while dispensing this in-depth dietary advice. He advised that beets had the highest amount of potassium, much to the amazement of his 10-12 thick crowd.

Then, very quickly and without notice the conversation switched to cleaning and cleaning products. One lady told of how she rinsed callaloo bush in a carefully titrated solution of bleach and water that she measured out with an old Trinidad Fruit Juices orange juice tin.

'Bharat Singh!' His discourse on food and nutrition was cut short by his turn to see the doctor.

As Dr. Persad was explaining the symptoms of kidney failure, I started to feel that I, too, might have had renal failure. Dizziness; low blood count; confusion; I didn't have the swelling in the ankle or the knees, so I discounted that the kidney hadn't failed —yet! Maybe my feelings might have fit the mold of another diagnosis, I reservedly thought.

Is when the doctor says, 'I realized an improvement in the creatinine levels in the blood from the last visit from the read out from the computer". I nearly fell off the chair!

Computer! Mt. Hope was using computers! Papayoooo- look ting!

Mt. Hope, like my Uncle Barry's kidneys, was improving! Only a four-hour ordeal this time, exclusive of the one hour 25 min wait at the pharmacy. Everyone had to wait their turn until their number was called. In the pharmacy, it was worse. Even doctors who were awaiting medicine to administer to patients awaiting root canal had to wait. The doctor assured me he didn't have staff to run these errands.

The analysis of my uncle's kidneys showed that the kidneys had been upgraded to a stage three, functioning at 33.7%. Improvement from stage four; functioning at 27%. I wanted to tell the last doctor who made us want to visit Dass Funeral Home after her pessimistic analysis to kiss my ass! But she wasn't there. A better eventuality for all involved. I wondered whether Mt. Hope's analysis on efficiency would read as impressively as my uncle's analysis.

We managed to stave off dialysis! Least the Iron Lady, (his sister, my aunt-the bed rock of the family) learnt how to sweeten his coffee with only sugar and not both sugar and condensed milk!

He was allowed none, not even the coffee. But she was not having that. Morning coffee was like manners, "good morning". So, my uncle managed to manage his sister's stubbornness and still escape dialysis and death. Testament to one's power of the mind and indefatigable human spirit. We walked out of Mt. Hope, the sun stinging our skin. It felt good, like life and possibilities, unlike the cold, cramped, endless waiting rooms in Mt. Hope. We lived to die another day.

The miraculous turn of events of monitoring one's constitution; feelings and or symptoms.

Only the lucky brave ones got diagnosed.

In The Fires (fuh sure) Of Hope and Prayer

~~~

"You are far too kind', swirled in my head like the little cigarette ringlets, first loose and unshaped and then pliable with less shape. For my colleague to attribute even an ounce of grace to me spoke more about his endurance than my kindness.

I was ready in the waiting room and when the matter got called, all kinds of foolishness started to happen with the screen, audio, and camera. It was not the first time I was privy to a judge, speaking frankly about his lack of patience for the incompetency of counsel, where I was counsel, able to hear but not be heard.

My colleague received high commendations for the manner in which the matter was concluded. All I ever hoped for was to maintain some level of composure, coherent sentences and not be thought of as a blubbering idiot. Higher aspirations like commendations from the Judge, was out of my league.

So, the internet went, I lost the connection and any hope of maintaining a decent reputation among my colleagues was shot to hell. My guarded composure was compromised; all sorts of fears were fighting for expression, hoping never to sound like a blubbering idiot.

Without warning, the internet snapped back on and I was able to see I was now present in court, with video and audio. "Ms. Jadoonanan, thank you for joining us", the judge announced. The blubbering idiot stepped forward. I was like a donkey in a circus! Late and embarrassed, I sheepishly apologized for my untimely arrival. Opposing counsel resembled what my idea of eloquence, preparedness, and finesse looked like. Not arrogant, but judicious and discreet. Well poised and unrehearsed. The man spoke with such sincerity in his tone that I was minded to accept his generosity, in terms.

The matter was tied up very nicely, not with my client in knots and uncertainty, but with the desired vindication and protection she sought. The piece of paper affords one at least the promise of justice, if you survived.

I was done with court for the day and was off to pick up a friend from the airport. I let out a loud snort on remembering snippets from our last conversations. Like the time he was telling me how men in Tobago 'fraid' dog and dead frog. Not that the story was a funny one at all, in fact it was quite the opposite. But

Trinis have the best sense of humor. Which is why it has been 59 years since we became independent, and we are singing the same themes, like a recurring nightmare through kaiso, calypso, and soca. Corruption, bacchanal and 'tiefin'!

We had a good sense of soothing ourselves from the horrors of the realities. More malls, more ports, more water taxis, more blimps —allyuh forget de blimp? All spelt equally; equal opportunity to tief! Water taxi sinking and they focused on "sunlight will kill covid". Iwer only singing "de people want water", but like dey deaf! Is year after year the man pleading. 59 years, sweet, sweet T& T, while the Stabilization and Heritage fund hemorrhaging.

Congestion; declining quality of life, more potholes and no water! But we jamming still! Failing democracy! A rise in non-disclosures, rise in jackassness; but we knew how to stomach the aches. This was we paradise! Davia also said he wanted to go Pan-a-ma, ma-ma! Because what it has over here, making trinis just go clear!

My friend said he was minding his own business, stopped to dig out a plant from the side of the road and some young fellas looked like they were routing, looking for trouble. Slowing down just as they approached him. "What kinda plant is that?" He said one look at the men who did not fit the profile of plant lover, with the tear drop tattoo and gold teeth and he sensed the four men in that silver Nissan Tida already had a conversation and the decision was descending as they slowly made their way crawling down the hill.

"Wild Riyo", my friend answered in the most aggressive, 'stay -far, don't- ask- me- no- more- question, yuh- mudda- cunt- lair, cause -you- not- interested- in- no- plant' voice which he could muster. Already making his way back, with the Riyo and his cutlass in hand.

But it looked like as they got closer, they could see inside my truck, two dogs; one Bully and one-half breed Husky; the other half we not sure of, but we pretty sure it's jackass! But he handsome fuh spite! So, he gets pardoned way too many times.

Anyway, the tear-drop tattooed driver, looked straight into the truck, two children and two dogs. Variables they may not have planned for. The children they could handle, but not the Bully. 'If is one thing bandit fraid, is dog bite and dead frog, especially if you put it on dey doorstep!' My friend reassured me. He said they were clear indicators of the unknown, that they dare not 'intafeeh' with. If yuh owe a man money and you decide you not paying, nail a dead frog on a tree nearest to he! If yuh get horn and yuh feel you know who it is, and yuh wanted vengeance- throw a dead frog on the horner-man bonnet!

At this point, with all this information, I wasn't sure if it was a work of fiction, is then the man schups an say, "real stores girl". "Man in Tobago fraid dead frog". He said it was a conversation stopper, the awkward kind. Like when yuh mudder find a g-string under she bed that is not hers and ask yuh fadda, "What is this"?

And well dog bite, no bandit going tru dat! They reached down the bottom of the hill. "Let me see"? My friend said he open the door so the full body and teeth of the Bully was shown, as he made his way into the truck, and with that, the tear eyed tattooed driver peeled off. Don't mind the dog is a Bully, whatever the breed, bandit does see pit bull. And is smile he smiling. But they don't know that.

Rise in crime; inflation; immigrant population; and mandatory vaccinations! "Captain, the seas are rough"! The Standard & Poor rated Trinidad as negative for growth and economic development, but they tell we a negative is a positive! -yuh see lie! No Rule of Law, no separation of powers; rise in tyranny!

But as a people, we bright and we have sense, we produce award winning coco and coffee; Nobel prize winners; Olympic medalists. We are forged from the love of liberty, liberty to hold our own thwarted perception of things. Which is why I chuckled first at the memory of my friend's story and didn't clad up in fear from the sense of security and safety they have stolen from us and traded it freely in the open market of "this our native land" for rampant mismanagement and the contract mafia. In fact, I laughed out loudly. How bizarre!

A Little Village Girl Comes to Herself

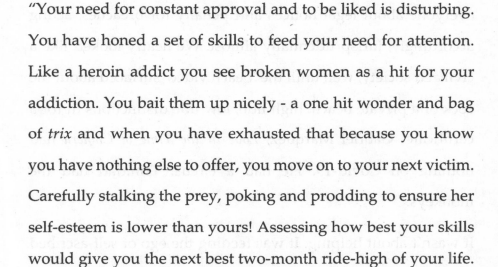

"Your need for constant approval and to be liked is disturbing. You have honed a set of skills to feed your need for attention. Like a heroin addict you see broken women as a hit for your addiction. You bait them up nicely - a one hit wonder and bag of *trix* and when you have exhausted that because you know you have nothing else to offer, you move on to your next victim. Carefully stalking the prey, poking and prodding to ensure her self-esteem is lower than yours! Assessing how best your skills would give you the next best two-month ride-high of your life. This isn't about broken women. This is the sadder story of a broken man, seeing an opportunity to satisfy his appetite for self-gratification. It isn't about helping; it is feeding the ego of self-ascribed importance. Broken attracts broken. That's the law of attraction." She said all of this, almost blue, from not taking a breath.

It had been six months of quarantine; on and off lockdowns, closed borders, no shark and bake at Maracas Bay, no currying duck at Caura River, legal notices and regulations frenzy. If no one had ever heard of the Public Health Act, they did now. 'Ordinance' rings of archaic language. The word 'ordinance' makes it sound so regal and authoritative. Covid-19 taught everyone about legal notices and penalty for breaches, acting accordingly, jurisprudentially almost. We nearly looked like a civilized society, well until the 'beach video' surfaced about the cock of a private beach: high tide; low tide distinctions fit for a certificate! Gabriel Marquez, *Love in the Time of Cholera* had nothing on Covid-19. He had a circus; Trinidad had the monkeys.

It wasn't about helping. It was feeding the ego of self-ascribed importance. Insecurities have a way of controlling us because they are so deep seated, like your best kept secret. So far down they have manipulated the anatomy of what they looked like even to its host. Insecurities undermined the very platform of the world we built for ourselves and eroded the quality of the existence. At some point you had to get back in that driver's seat (or not) and steer the course of where you were going. You also must not get carried away by insecurities that plagued progress. Identification was key to understanding the weakness. Looking in the mirror and not into another victim's eyes and asking why am I doing this? Face yourself. Teach yourself how you are enough, that you are the love you want; that you are that security and support you seek. Build you! Not break others because of your fears that you are "not good enough." A lot of people talk very loudly and say nothing. If, with the end in mind, you would never start before you fixed that reflection in the mirror.

When you change the way you look at things, the things you look at change; not my words! It's the voice of Dr. Wayne Dyer. A lot to be said for practice of positive affirmations. When we heal ourselves, the very situations we look at get transcribed from a change in perspective. If we heal those parts of us that are broken, we don't see and/or attract what is broken. We can assist without adding to the demise of self or others around.

Self-revolutionary! The Power of Self, not the fake self of little 'I' the ego, but the real essence of who you are, your higher self. But it takes courage to invest in the transformation of oneself. Mental and physical fortitude to walk through the valley of the shadow of death! Warriors who have rooted their journey in the knowing that victory will be theirs and everything is always working out in divine order know this. They also know when to draw their sword and when to retreat.

Find your power walk in your strengths. Uplift and inspire, but don't do it for the ego and self-gratification. That's why my *dharma* says renounce the fruit of action and "doership" of action. Give to a higher power so you don't lose yourself in the little 'I' or ego. Remain a simple servant to humility and service. The high science of this philosophy isn't easily understood. It is a lifelong mission. But it makes living very livable.

The *Nirvana Shatakam* comes to mind. I digress; a road map of how my mind works would lead you down a rabbit hole! It's about living in freedom; the form of eternal consciousness. Your higher self speaks to answers of what self-love is. Look back; stand in appreciation for what you have been fortunate to accomplish. A sense of gratitude should start to emanate from the heart. That's the start of self-love. And, well, ego just beats his chest as he walks around whichever playground he is allowed! Ego is necessary in this transactional world of duality but keep it in its place. Don't let it run the show. Act from a place of love, not fear. Then figure this out: Why am I acting? Out of my own fears; my own insecurities? Could any good come from that? Before you fix the world, make sure your inner world is wholesome and healthy and that you are vibrating in alignment with your higher self.

Yes, yes. We get it! The Nirnavna Shatakam comes to mind! A good thing too, as the gentleman who seemed to have a weakness for needing to comfort battered women sent via text that he was distracted by another woman. "She is divorced and in an abusive relationship," he texted. Like the particulars of a new case. A cynic was in session! I suggested to him he put up a sign, "Shandy Lane, shelter for the needy." I was serious! I was very serious about my sense of humor. How could he not have been distracted? He didn't know how past life events were hell bent on teaching her invaluable lessons!

The players in this game of life forced her to find her value, see her worth, learn the lesson, become the warrior, maintain equipoise, subdue the ego, earn the virtues, live the beatitudes. She had a friend in Life. When people shut her out, brought disappointment to her and took away loved ones, over and over, she became that solace within herself. The strength in her own chest. Life was so pleased with its product that it presented this unfortunate soul to test her.

She was so odd, not in any need of a thing, a chase for nothing, she stood still, she knew who she was. Wasn't carried away by the intransigence of life's fleeting pleasures; she was solitude itself. She became so reverent with herself that even before her tongue spoke, it requested permission from the mind and senses. She subjected herself to a rigorous reflection ritual of thought, word, action, synchronicity. Lord *Krsna* was her only counsel, her only love, the only pastimes she cared to revel in. She had no need, no want, no desire.

So, this poor poor man, who knew only his strengths in comforting broken women, met upon this little village girl. When his eyes fell upon her, he only saw through his own broken window a weak, meek village girl. She appeared as a slip of a thing. He didn't see her carrying the weight of her experiences in her stride or in her robust power to wield a sword. He didn't see the strength in her silence.

Of course, he became distracted. He was not needed. He needed to be needed. But this little village girl grew unsheltered from the comforts of two-parent families. She had to become that encourager of herself. Or was it the trauma ever propelling her from the harsh realities that greeted her? She had to find motivation to exist in the shirking world around her; after all, the matriarchal setup was geared just to eke out a survival.

Dreams and aspirations were for the neighbors' children and the children of her mother's and aunt's fancy clients, those kids who jumped out of their Mercedes Benz and Nissan Laurels, sometimes in their checkered private school uniforms or in their colored sequin tops with jeans and the little bags they carried. She looked down at her clothes. They were clean, they had to be clean, but it was a tee-shirt sponsored by one of the locals who had made it big in the US, and it read "Sims Mini Mart." There was nothing glamorous or sequin-worthy in a convenient store! Once she was offered lip gloss, and it smelt so good, the little woman-girl exclaimed, "It's not to eat, it's for your lips!" She knew that. Duh!

As the appointed baby sister, she was happy to put down the broom for sweeping other people's hair. It was definitely the grossest experience of all time! But sometimes, she would touch it, the long hair, the colored hair, only the girl's hair. Men's hair was icky and sharp and cut even when it had no agenda.

I was the appointed babysitter, taking these privileged kids to the back to pick cherries, plums, mangoes, while the peroxide worked its magic. This was their frolic; this was her existence. It would take decades after for the little girl to see what she had was heaven. They came for a fleeting glance to experience her heaven. To think they were the lucky ones; foolish little Indian girl!

This poor foolish little Indian girl became reticent. She started to see how the world treated little Indian girls. Our thoughts, less engaged. Unless of course we insisted on being heard, in which case we were titled as giving trouble, unruly; a disgrace to the family's reputation. We were not picked for cricket, although Orissha from down the street was just as good or even better than the captain himself! We weren't picked to perform the last rites for our parents. We were not given our mother's maiden names. We were paid less. Our voices were almost not heard. Thank God for Arhundati Roy; Indira Gandhi; Margaret Thatcher, the iron lady herself, and, in recent times, Jacinda Ardern!

Dr. Ramnarine on talking to her about trauma, at one of her visits at the Ishtara center said, "It was an opportunity to propel your consciousness at a very young age." It didn't feel that way. *Opportunity* was something that was supposed to feel good and exciting, like cake on a birthday. This was dark and foreboding, like no cake on a birthday. Anyway, thank God she was at a ripe age of about 23 when he mentioned it first; trauma?

She marveled at how she got to be described as one who "suffered trauma." That sounded fit for TV characters' problems, not hers. Little Indian girls didn't have trauma, they lived in the real world. Things happened and we just continued with life as if everything was normal. Anyway, I wondered what she did with this trauma up until 23, when she had first heard of it. Where did she put it? Stick a pin!

She carried the Devi, Maha Kali! She knew how to do battle. She knew how battles were fought. She toyed with the dictum of Sun Tzu's "to win without battle is best"; this was at variance with his supreme knowledge. This was how quintessentially she became what she became. Never accepting anything as her own, not even "truth". Well, not until she explored and dove into the things and came out, albeit through the devil's asshole! But she was able to give proper experiential accounts of things, events, and people. She was strong and earned her legs to carry her strength. She fought.

Sun Tzu might not have been pleased his life's work aided in battle, a battle of a different kind. She waged war within herself! Not the negative self-talk that self-loathing comes from. No! This was her lining up of her enemies as they roared and her severing off the heads! They fell apart; the heads, one head at a time! She was powerfully aligned with the power that created worlds! She had learnt the art of war. Sun Tzu would be pleased.

Daddy Went To California

The flashing lights from the four fire trucks flooding the street blurred my vision. They muted the surroundings. I closed my eyes. Behind closed eyes, things/events could be altered to feel a sense of normalcy. Ten minutes ago, they were watching the popular local cultural TV show *Mastana Bahar* and it was time for the contestant to 'pick a pan'. This is when my mom was interrupted by Mr. Andrews, our next-door neighbor, cautioning that something might have happened to my daddy, Sam.

I watched from the bottom of the stairs, my mom leaping down. She passed me but didn't acknowledge me.

"No Robert! No Robert!" she shouted.

"It's not ok, how could it be, ok?!" I heard her lamenting in the most powerless assertion I had ever heard.

I wasn't watching the TV show. I was looking for Dad. I had found him. Mr. Andrews had found me.

My sisters and I watched the scene unfold like a TV show, only we were the characters with no scripts. My mom sat on the road, her head in her hands. I wondered in my silence as to why she was so distraught. I knew how to operate the mechanism to lift and lower the hoist. But I didn't think she wanted to hear from me, just yet. The men in uniform were attempting the task at hand. Surely, they would get it up.

As I watched from Aunty Pat's window (another next-door neighbor), the sun long gone and the night set, it was evident the men in uniform needed more help as the street became even more crowded, with police vehicles and then the ambulances and helicopters. The flashing frenzy from all the different colored lights made the night's sky seem ablaze. People were everywhere.

I remembered telling Aunty Pat I knew how to lift the hoist and asking why I wasn't allowed to go over and show them; and that they needed to hurry because Daddy was being squeezed and would have been hurting. When I saw him earlier that afternoon, he didn't say anything of the pain or discomfort. He also didn't respond to my finding his hiding spot. Maybe he didn't like that I found him or maybe he was a sore loser. But how could he be, when at every card game, he would let me win, knowing fully well I had been cheating! I don't think he was playing our favorite game, hide n' seek that afternoon, rather, he just lay very still. I also found it passing strange that his 'chuck', a piece of 2x4 wood, his, safety-first-self-ISO, was leaning against the wall and not where it would normally be when he was working under the hoist.

I remember Christopher and Aaron who had accompanied me that afternoon to seek Dad's permission to go riding, because Mom had said it was too late; 5:30pm was too late! I remember them saying there was blood leaking from the truck, dripping into a puddle. I promptly told them that was just the 'red oil' which trucks used.

They clearly knew nothing of trucks and how they operated. I did. I was fortunate to accompany Dad on Saturday mornings to the quarries. I knew how he operated the hoist. Plus, we were nearly the same height, so I could easily stand up and mash the clutch too! When he pulled out our breakfast of sada roti from the cooler, I knew what was on the agenda; spelling and 'times-tables'! We got up to four 'times tables'. I had to do the rest on my own.

My mom was not interested in 'times tables'. I remembered telling her some months after that I was up to my nine 'times tables'. She did not look impressed. In fact, from the vacant expression that washed over her face, it made me feel like she was worried I was probably behind on things and I hated spelling. So I avoided my mom as much as a seven-year-old could have. She, too, maintained her distance, but at least I was still in Trinidad, Caledonia Road. It felt like she had taken up residence on a distant planet. She went to work, dropped us to school, clothed us and ensured books were in our bags and food on the table. Her boss told her she had to wear the lipstick.

I did see his elbow bent, looking like a dried coconut. It is what prompted me to climb up the truck to see where the rest of his body was, as I had circled several times calling out, "Daddy, Daddy I catch you!" but there was no answer, remember?

He was wearing his blue shorts. I could see that clearly. He still didn't answer me, my request to go riding seemed to have fallen on deaf ears and my jubilation of wining, 'hide n' seek' went unnoticed. It was when Mr. Andrews saw me halfway up the new Nissan D6, brand spanking new, brightest orange in all the milky way, that he called out to me saying, "that was not a safe place to play". I assured him Dad was right there and pointed to where I saw him lying in the blue shorts. Mr. Andrews had asked me again, "Where is your dad?" After my answer, he crossed the street to meet with the three of us. He urged the other two to head home and accompanied me to mine.

I overheard that my eldest sister Leesha would be returning to Trinidad and my other sister Sunita set out with Uncle Dips (another next-door neighbor) by car to start informing the family members of what had happened. Sunita was 17, she was in the early stages of attempting to prepare meals. That day she tried her hand at salmon and rice; pink salmon from the tin. She was saying out loud how she saw him at about 3:30 in the afternoon. She told him to come and eat. She, too, seemed to be trying to go back in her mind to when the thing was understandable. However, in her state of confusion she did what she had to do. Like learning to operate the lawnmower; Daddy taught her. My other sister, Tricia, retreated to her room.

I had been trying to find him since then. Seems like he liked 'hide n' seek' more than I do. I looked for him in all the wrong places, very similar to when you are looking for love or God. A seven-year-old's mind is not quite equipped to process what death means, even when it was laid before her real, physical eyes. Seven-year-olds simply do the best they could to manage; so, the morning of the funeral when I glanced at my reflection in the mirror, just before heading out, they were shouting downstairs, "The body reach!"

I used that as my signal to get into position; I didn't know where this was though. I looked at myself for confirmation of what was going on around me. I needed my seven-year-old self to steady my seven-year-old self.

"Dead," I said aloud.

"Daddy died".

"Daddy died?"

A conversation ensued between myself and my reflection. One of us tried to convince the other that while something had happened, other things were happening. The reflection believed the seven-year-old when she instructed, "He is not dead, he is in Miami; Biscane Bouvlevard." The reflection listened attentively to the pact that was being drafted and was receptive in receiving the programming. The instructions continued, "I will look after you and keep you safe". I am still having that conversation with that reflection at 42 years old.

I heard my eldest sister, Leesha ask on walking through the kitchen doors, "Where is Melissa?" I was so excited to see her and it seemed from her first question she was just as eager to see me. Never mind she was bawling just moments before, "My daddy, where is my daddy?!"

I left him in California!" She crumbled into my mom's arms. Standing still so stately in her white pants and white jacket. She was the most beautiful girl in my world through my eyes. My sister Leesha. She was a celebrity. She travelled, we all travelled, but she was the star.

I walked up to my lady-in-waiting and awaited her move. Her arms opened to hug me. "What did you bring for me?" seemed like the most natural of questions to pose to the traveler. She unwrapped a little brown bear, whose limbs could be manipulated to turn in any direction. It wasn't hard like a GI Joe figurine, it was soft, like teddy bears should be, but it moved. So very strange. This was how Tricia played with me. Well one of the ways. I agreed to being chained and tied to the gate like a dog. I didn't agree to being left out in the 12 o'clock sun; fine dining restaurant games like orange juice in a champagne glass; homemade table tennis board with two barrels and a piece of 'pitch pine' for a net; never ending yo-yo competitions, so many games!

She would take off the bear's red jacket, put it on his head, like a headdress through the ears, spin his limbs around, so that his once bushy tail ended up looking like a penis, with over grown pubic hairs. "Rambo teddy," I was told is what he became. Rambo teddy, the truant bear. Not fit to be bedded with care bears; cabbage patch dolls, albeit the fake ones which Daddy got for me from the market, or my 3ft. walking doll Daddy brought me back from Miami on his reconnecting flight from California on his last trip.

She had cut the walking doll's hair and hid her from me and hung my cabbage patch doll out the window for me to see.

She stayed in her room. Leesha had to go to her.

The Aftermath of Storms

L is for Love, D is for Dotish.

That skin is like the never-ending silkiness of the Nile. Stretching across miles of uncharted territory of my mind's eye. The skin that chants the mantra that forces my submission into oblivion. Oh, for the love of God and men - I was immersed in the depth of the beauty of the undulating landscape and the pull of his energy that beckoned my every fibre. My eyes could not unsee where my thoughts had brought me. Take me to that place where your eyes soften and you yield to the command on my fingertips; where you reach for me, only me; want me, only me; feel me, only me.

Oh, for that muse of fire, that would ascend and cause chaos within the confines that once held strong and steadfast amid your storms!

You are the storm that threatens to breach the gates of my sanity.

This was the incision. He took my hand in his, unbuttoned his shirt with the other, and slowly carried my hands across his chest.

The feel of his skin evoked memories that were unleashed without warning. My mind became unsettled and restless. My breathing uncontrolled. 'The table was cold, stainless steel cold'. I wanted to take my other hand and cover his and say something. But I was riveted to my chair, trying to breathe, and shut off what I already knew couldn't be turned off. I did try, for two years.

I could hear his voice, causing a familiar chaos. I didn't know what he was saying anymore.

He smelt like the air I wanted to breathe. I wanted to breathe him in. I wanted him coursing through my veins and on the tip of my tongue. I wanted to taste him.

I was happy to live within the void of the memories. Well, not happy, but prepared to go without; remain unquenched. But since it was I who put the full stop in the middle of our paragraph, I thought I could remove it; worse could happen - it could turn into a comma.

He was the same pleasant, cultured, beautiful man I had no choice but to extricate from my timeline, two years ago.

Like an unrivalled Mapepire, he was carefully camouflaged with discretion and mystery and beautifully adorned with charm and that magnetic pull. His voice and smile and that mouth that curved effortlessly into a smile that led from the comforts of familiarity to my demise. Jesus knew I loved him. All of him. He should have gone to hell! Or at least seen the depths of it. I didn't know that he didn't. I didn't know what his world spun into or how it cascaded.

He seemed to be healed. The scar across his chest was bumpy. But even the blasted scar couldn't disturb the disruption in my thoughts, that that skin could cause.

I heard him in my ear, on my neck, against my body; pressed against my breasts. His hands held my sanity; and his lips, top and bottom threatened to undo the two years of barricaded reinforced protection that silence kept.

I tried to protest.

But my body didn't even put up a fight. My mind in its usually carefully crafted deduction of risks was blank. My body succumbed.

If even I lied to myself; I would lie again, and again and again.

'Red gyal goh send yuh mad'. The song was right! Red yuh dead, yes!

Who could withstand that? Not even Mary Magdalene with all her Hail Marys and stations of the cross could stop his ten fingers from digging into my back.

Nobody had the vaccine for that.

I loved him. Two years of retributive abstinence had now been reduced to two bodies, admitting if only for those moments the truth of a thing that would never be spoken.

"Can I come for coffee?'

"Of course, my doors are always open."

"When now? In the morning?"

"Whenever you like, whenever you felt you couldn't resist the aroma and blend of my daily brew."

7:30am he was outside my gate. He had the same black van. I didn't forget the tumble of that engine, everything tumbling along and, in its way, gladly. I smiled. Two years ago, we said goodbye, well kind of.

Anyway, this was the now, that was the past.

That smile could stop traffic. The warmth of his embrace and softness of his cheeks on mine was like the settling of debts and the renegotiation of compounded interest.

This man was beautiful, Satan couldn't deny it. But God the father knew how he was a royal cunt and how that beauty did his bidding, effortlessly. You wouldn't blame him; he balanced what I needed and gave without my ever asking. What I remained without was my own fault. Arrogant as a peacock and fucked up; a fucking Judas! I never saw one human being personify so many conundrums. Regard for life for every living creature, except me! I was left for dead. Like roadkill. No phone calls, no apology. Nasty mudda cunt!

I hated him for what I always suspected he was. Unkind? No, he wasn't. He was stuck between the devil's asshole and acted out of cowardice. But he wasn't a coward either. What was he? Honest. Brutally honest.

So, I put a muther fucking full stop. You ent see me or wah!?

I was not dealing with no body fucking conscience and their staggering statistics.

Fuck you!

But then Mommy died.

And I was made to deal with big people things. Things I refused to want to address. So, I texted him telling him my truth, that he was dead to me and how life made me re-evaluate the many, many things I once thought I understood.

Love was not one.

How's yuh mom?

Dead.

Is how he spin around in the kitchen and grabbed my hand. I could never forget the look in his eyes. He was never one to let anything show. That day it slipped out.

I wasn't angry anymore. I had calmed down. I learnt plenty of things, mostly about myself. And about the ways of love. How love wasn't selfish nor possessive; love was patient, love was kind. Corinthians. I learnt through the fires of hell what love was, is, and ought to be.

Honesty taught me how to love.

So, love is forgiving?

Forgiveness in a time of Covid? Maybe it was the fevers or the stench of death lingering around our lives.

I didn't know what caused it, but people who tief from people were forgiven in debts and deaths. It was indeed spectacularly an absurd series of events.

Imagine, a man who tief from you and your sister was welcomed back into the fold and treated like the Bollywood movie 'Singh is King'! And people who didn't tief anything but your worries and stress away, were treated like the perpetrators.

How bizarre!

Is the 'chirren fadda', so I guessed that ironed out all the explanations and justifications that were needed to absolve the thieving. No thieving meant no thief. Because the 'chirren fadda' was still around, nobody threw away the key. So, through love, a thief was exonerated.

So, love has discretion?

But imagine being a thief and not knowing it.

I gave all I could. I didn't know what more I could give. What I couldn't give, they took my self-respect; my sense of belonging I managed to carve out for myself; alone. My joy, my comforts, my ease, my happiness.

It all stood still, like one big second hand that just wouldn't tick the time away.

And I was labelled the thief!

Voodoo.

But who was the real 'tief', who took the unity that once exited. Which greedy mother fucker, manipulative cunt hole, dictated like moths to flames; the disunity that we faced.

Humph! And I was the thief. Working like a slave! Do this; pick up that; collect that; drop that; give that.

But I did that, honestly? Out of love, regard, and respect.

So, love out of obligation?

Boy. Is real ting I see this rounds.

Love does make people do real 'dotishness'.

Love should be a crime against humanity.

People should be found guilty of love and fucking sentenced to write in 100 words what love is; what it is to love and what is it to show love; with their fingernail!

Love could never be a defence.

I undermined her and criticized her because I loved her; I slapped her because I loved her; I drank poison because I loved him.

It was fucking twisted!

If love was so good, how did so much wrong come from it?

Love yuhself!

But if love was selfish, Corinthians had it wrong.

Who was I to say.

Forgive them father for they know not what they do.

The Art of Gaming

The fire that blazes deep within, parts her thighs.

Her body that is warm and flushed is glowing with anticipation. It rests in the hands of opportunity and skilful manoeuvring of ordinary words.

This game of chess has been ongoing since the players decided to play. But the game is afoot, and the players are real and the game is their life - of balance; artful manipulation of the mundane to subdue the unruffled mind. The warriors unsheathed their swords.

This fire is all consuming; it burned down a village, left nothing in its way, except the gossip of the villagers as gossip travels faster than a raging fire.

It destroyed her marriage, her mind her image her perceptions her world. This fire took her place in the world.

Fire is necessary but too much fire turns things and people to ash.

Fire in the head; stomach; loins! Fire, fire!!

In waiting she buried her thoughts in him. How his strong, rigid yet yielding body would connect with hers.

She was rushing.

For he was not what lived in her imagination of the picture of carnal redemption.

He was shy, and beautiful. So beautiful. Never asked for a thing that wasn't readily available for him.

Coffee? Tea? Me? ... I was always tempted to ask in that order.

He would never give away any sign he was desirous of igniting fires.

It was a game of wits and control, quiet lust and calm proclamation.

'You have oil?' Was the bravest I had ever heard of him. Whether he was rappelling down 259 feet mountains; kayaking in the open Atlantic Sea; swimming with sharks, mountain biking and clavicle breaking, Amazon explorer or cave dweller. He was jungle Jesus!

And I was his Mary Magdalene; if only in my head!

74

So, sex and lower-level needs; love making and all that expression of flesh, was not spoken of.

He was content to eat bread rolled from my hands and nothing more, or nothing less. We did a balancing dance of the most beautiful display of the only kind of love we knew, but had never spoken. For love is borne from sacrifice and devotion. Anyone worth suffering for ... etc... we had heard the lectures; lived the sermons. Our suffering was not insufferable. It was a welcomed way of life. Our life was achieving balance, together and separate. This was another station of our cross, in learning the art of balance.

So anyway, words were not the love language either of us knew how to use. Words were borne from trickery, to say a thing didn't mean a thing. To mean a thing, you didn't have to say a thing.

That is where we lived, right in that in-between. Words had a way of killing things, choking things to death with its need for meaning and interpretation. I loved how he made me choke with my hair wrapped in his hands. I didn't need words to tell me what he meant or what he was feeling. I was moving this powerful body under me, like the Pyramids of Giza! He had three. His skin, his strength, and his stare. This body that had gone to where no man had gone before; diving in the Red Sea, Thailand and Malaysia; dared to explore my hidden recesses; legs that mountaineered to the abode of Lord Shiva in the Himalayas, mounted my back. I was the surf that the surfer was riding. His knowledge of navigating rip currents was instrumental once he found himself tangled in my grip. He dared to chart a course to know my mind. A worthy endeavour.

We connected our energies for higher experiences but maintained separate paths. This was how we danced the world away.

We didn't speak of things we knew; for words had a devious intent; misguided at most. The moment it was spoken and thus known was to have it on its way to die a sure death. Better to keep some things tightly guarded.

The fire was blazing, excessive throbbing; unbearable heat; what remedy you suggest, is the answer to this torment?

The poetry in my head while we danced our thoughts perfectly hidden; for none to see.

Sifting through the mundane profundities, while that fire blazed my presence away. In my head, if he could see just what he did to me, with that smile directed to me.

Quickened heartbeat; irregular breathing, 'Sugar this morning?

Proffer a proposal before I internally combust!

But none to see, my breath unbated, I swallowed the evidence of my fire blazing.

Then with no warning, "will you put some oil on my back?"

I could feel what I swallowed coming back up. Careful to seem uninterested in the Pyramids of Giza but only to serve, I was able to utter words that do not betray my truest intent and with careful constraint, I managed, "Would you like to lie down? My bed is made (and waiting for you), I'll come up in a bit".

He sent his knight out. His queen exposed. He is the braver. He has won and was now deserving.

I could have answered his question, "Yes, I have oil?"

But was that the answer he was hunting for?

How could he have known of the fire blazing and the torment? There was no smoke.

No soot, no smell, no ash, no destruction; yet!

Words added fuel to fire. But the inborn trickery of the use of the words came from the meaning we ascribed to them. Words were always innocent. We transcribed our heaven burdens of expectations using words not fit for purpose. But where was the treachery? The words found the meaning within the greater picture. How? Were words magical? Words were potent. Words gave us the strength of courage to ask for what our feeble egos could not.

Words disguised and protected. Harboured and nurtured.

As I made my way up the stairs, highway to heaven to my bed, I smiled. The pounding in my chest had returned. The Pyramids of Giza, all three on my bed.

"Will you put some oil on my head?"

He had played his queen's Indian.

Blowing in the Wind

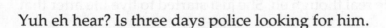

Yuh eh hear? Is three days police looking for him.

The last reports the police received from the villagers was that he was driving the new Nissan Navara Shanti bought him, bejewelled with gold and adorned with all the religious threads and all the gods around his neck; together with the one-inch rope he was found hanging from. He needed protecting, *maljoe* was the least of his worries. He was a good son. Obedient and kind to his mother. But no one knew outside his set parameters what connected the thoughts he thought and the things he thought out and did.

They say Shanti like she take-even, she walking up and down de road bawling out, "Raj, why yuh gone and leave meh? Oh, Gawd, what I Goh do now with myself?" The boy eh even cremate, and she getting on in this kinda way. I doh know what does go on with some people. Shanti, like she has no respect, not for the dead or even the living.

She sitting down in the middle ah the road in the night. Is only wen we hear the screeching brakes and the screaming; we know is Shanti. Making all kinda deal with God, to take she instead of the boy.

But it mussie real though eh. She just started to live life after that no-good drunk, beating she within an inch of she life, finally take he last drink. The same inch that put Raj in he box. They find him, blunt force trauma to the head, at the foot of the stairs. No investigation. They just wrap that one up quick quick quick!

She was so proud of Raj. But I remember Raj telling me a story about when his *mudda* carried him up in the hills by St. Ann's. They left him right there for observation. The white lady teacher in the school had recommended to Shanti that she take him there. He said, he tell the doctors that he felt safer inside those walls, because in there, he could just be who he wanted to be. Most times he only wanted to be himself. He says the people inside the walls all had their own little worlds, like wining pods; everybody was designated a space, no one encroached, and everybody was happy; or at least their construct of happy.

But yuh didn't find no body trying to tell nobody what they should be singing, wearing, loving or praising. It was all man for themselves. Each in his own world, where all was given the same due regard and medicine. Perfect balance.

He say when he come out from behind the walls, he finds the people was acting in a kinda way, that he thought them needed medicine. Everybody had an opinion about what the other was doing. Criticism, complaining, animosity, jealously. Pure hate, it didn't feel like it was a safe place to be, worse, to be yourself, or express your own sense of you-ness. He had a funny way he used to talk. It was nice to hear how he put things across.

I don't know if Shanti goh leave the roti shop to run. She cyar handle stove and fire right now, wit whey she mind is nah. Raj was she eyeball. Pride and joy. Scholarship to study medicine. It was as if Shanti got a new lease on life and will to live when Raj says he going university. Poor thing didn't even know what academic distinction was but was smiling like Guy Smiley overflowing with happiness when the boy walk across de stage and they put de medal around his neck. More ting 'round he neck; he was done so skinny.

He had done stop the cricket with the fellars, long before this thing happened. They say he was busy beating book, not he gal! She was highfalutin, from the East; Santa Margarita. I never had cause to talk to she. But she used to bat in she crease when she come by the roti shop to buy roti and exchange books with Raj.

Is one time Shanti come out with the *belna* quarrelling with Raj. She wanted him to hurry up; that the curry burning. Wit de look Raj give she, she quietly lowered the *belna* and told him to come when he finish.

I was just as confused as Shanti. The boy was a good boy. I didn't know what I wudda do if I was Shanti and I find my son like that. Bright bright future, bright ideas, bright as a bulb, but too bright it looks like! The funeral was tomorrow. They had to watch Shanti, she need medicine because she unpredictable.

Raj say he used to feel invisible and as if no one could hear him when he talk. He was so far in his head, I didn't know if he use to be talking at all. He described that he felt like he was floating tru life, disconnected to people and things. I remembered him saying people were too loud and close to him, too aggressive and opinionated.

Whatever the case, Shanti needed prayers now more than ever. I didn't know how she, or if she could ever recover from that day she found him. Is how she pull down the white sheets from the line, sun blazing in she eye, she had to squint, and when she looks up, she sees Raj tangled in the Cha tagine tree. She blinked and started questioning Raj, bawling in a kind of hysteria bout why he in the back in for so long? That people looking for him; that everybody worried; to come dong; that the shop closed three days now!

I didn't know how long she was in the back with the body, blowing in the wind, but when the police reach, they find Shanti hugging Raj feet. She was pleading, wailing, "come dong nah beta!"

Flight of the Ibis

～～～

Lord Krishna left Vindravan thousands of years ago. It was the end of that era. He succumbed to the curse of Gandhari, the wife of Dhritarastra. Lord Krishna and all his subjects would be destroyed just as her 100 sons had died on the battlefield of Kurushetre with Lord Krishna leading the vicars.

This was during the Dvapara Age, or the third quarter of existence of one age of Brahma, as postulated by Sri Yukteshwar in his book, The Holy Science. The end of that age ushered in the Kali age, the current age, where it is marked by a decline of morals and God consciousness, with an increase in materialism, technology, and an overall disinterest in the mastery of self and any subjects connected there to.

It was amidst this Kali yuga era that Lord Krishna happened upon a glitch in the timeline. If you are familiar with the sacred texts, the Lord for the kali age is meant to be Kalki and it was not his time yet, but Krishna's has passed.

Hindus are great at having a God for everything. The Wind God; Sun God; God of Wealth; God of Strength; God of Obstacles, and the list goes on... They prayed to everything, so to simplify the worship, not the intention or devotion, they would create a God in the present for the God of the Future, and make him the God of all things for that era. It is indeed testament to "Where is Bramha not?" I think their Gods have a great sense of humour, because in the end, as in the beginning, they claim no name or form, no beginning and no end.

Anyhow, because nothing happens without his will, Krishna found himself gasping for clean air in the front seat of a Toyota Hilux. It was stuck in horrendous traffic; the roads were impassable. Initially he thought he might have been on the moon. Good heavens, Lord Krishna looked up as if to ask Lord Shiva, the Lord of Destruction, whether he had been caught in the middle of the Nataraja (the dance of destruction!), or if he ended up in error in a lower dimension state of existence, for it felt chaotic and pointless.

Lord Shiva, who was sitting deep in meditation at the top of the Himalayas, smiled and communicated to his Lord that he was in fact on a little island called Trinidad. An island, not in your traditional sense of sun, sea, and sand, but rather, a little melting pot. A pot for bacchanal, corruption, misfeasance in public office, child molesters, rapists, and murders!

Trinidad has passed through the hands of many who have all left their mark on her. She is part of a twin with Tobago. She also boasts of exotic locations like, Parlatuvier, Charlotteville, Laventille, Chaguanas (bustling with activity, bargain masters, brimming with dhalpouri and markets) and Caroni, the epicentre for the island's national bird as well as its major food source, the little crabs. She jots out to meet the Caribbean Sea which is teeming with life both below and above its surface.

The twin island Republic, independent with her own Parliament, Head of State, and her own currency, floating, amidst the post-colonial bloodshed. Though many believed her currency to be one of wine and jam! It was owing to the rich diverse culture of its people. Trinidad has its very own instrument, the steel pan! Never mind the intellectual property issues that have plagued it.

"We are the most southerly of the Caribbean isles, home to steel band, calypso, and soca. Land of the Hummingbird, Scarlet Ibis and Cocrico; at least that's how I remembered the introduction when Trinidad and Tobgao Television (ttt) was singing on.

A quick search for Lord Krishna on Google revealed minimally what he had hoped to find. Answers to why the state of existence seemed to be depraved, devoid, and desolate. He decided to ask the driver of the Hilux some of his questions.

"Your chanting of Bhagavad Gita is very much improved".

Screeching brakes, crashing sounds, a five-car smash up, and cusses from left, right, and centre!

Lord Krishna sensed this was not a good time to ask his questions and apparated away to see the mangrove covered with Scarlet Ibis, just a stone's throw away. After the insufferable ordeal of exchanging insurance information, police station visits, and all the judgemental steers and head shaking connotating, "a-woman-again" from the on-coming traffic macos the accident created. The driver of the Hilux putting her thoughts back together and exclaiming, "What de ass really just happen here??" She went into a whirl wind of epic confusion just before the cacophony of the five-car smash up!

"Lord Krishna?"

"Yes?" She fainted.

Of course, she imagined the occurrence! Lord Krishna was not in her front seat. I mean he could be seated in the throne of her heart or centred at her spiritual third eye. But to have been physically present, sitting in her vehicle, on blazing hot leather seats, warmed up by the morning sun beating in, was just insane!

I mean omniscient and omni present, metaphysical and physical, why was I limiting the energies? What energies? If by energies I meant imagination, then ok. I tried my best to process the thoughts through all the filters of my mind. It was no use, the central nervous system was in overdrive due to an overload of sequencing of events and no answers, no solutions! I think I broke it. Without further thinking, and wrestling with the questions surfacing in my mind, I broke free of being in my head and asked, reluctantly, yet in the shakiest but sincerest voice, as if I were standing in line waiting to receive medicine to stabilise a condition in a mental asylum: "What is wrong with me?"

A quick glance over at the passenger's seat, and she was reminded how ludicrous this scene appeared. She shook her head in disbelief and turned on the radio for some form of normalcy. The heavens must think I am pagal!

She went to bed, flummoxed at the day's occurrences. She would have either had to take a vacation or see a therapist. And seeing she had very limited resources for either, she had hoped that a good night's sleep might at least would be a starting point for clarity of mind.

The candle flickering on the wall made shadows of little pixies, the mountain of un-ironed school shirts looked more intimidating in the night's darkness; perfectly monstrous in all respects! Tomorrow for sure. She pushed the stack of books, remotes, and her spectacles to the next side of the bed, blew out the candles and hoped for the best. My excess was going to go up- again!

I swallowed hard, my heart beating though my mouth; I was not understanding what was happening. I could not make sense of it, nor was I scared. My body was overwhelmed. I had awakened to pee. It was about four a.m. and sitting on my bed was Lord Krishna, playing his flute. I heard nothing, this was a dream where I got up to pee. Now I felt stupid to go pee. Was I dead? Did we have to pee in the afterlife too? Stupid question it seemed, but I was being practical. But I could not move. Was I having sleep paralysis? This was me in my dream with a vivid imagination-right?

Why do people do things in my name? I don't ask for anything, I need nothing but yet still people put me at the root of their sorrows; sacrifices; promises. I cannot interfere with the path you have chosen. You have selected these experiences to help in your expansion of the universe as designed by you. But when the weight of your choices gets unbearable for you to manage, your objectives become blurred by your tears. You become weakened and lose your determination to grow, not always; but your waiver. This is when I try to assist you, but if you are not in the vicinity of the vibration I am sending, it would not reach you.

It was like losing your ring down the road, but you are looking for it under the streetlight up the road!

We seemed stupid given that analogy. I wanted to defend us, but I could not talk. Sleep paralysis! This condition seemed to have been moulded by the devil's own hands!

That we should respond with love to others; that we should treat each other with gentility and kindness and no judgment, as we are each on a different journey for self-actualization, and self-transcendence, but different paths. All lead to one.

Why was I being schooled on kindergarten ethics of how to get along 101? I suspected because 5000 years later we still were doing it wrong, and technology was not helping us. In fact, it was crippling the children; isolating civilization; segregating and weakening the human spirit, dismantling that which was meant to be the very fabric to spring forth from and make a joyful noise.

I thought of the dream I had and smiled. It was so reassuring. There was so much love. I felt drenched in love and support of the whole world. It was weird, like I was on a micro dose of psilocybin and had reconnected with the energies of the all sustaining consciousness.

I walked down the stairs and through the kitchen. I opened the door to my office; my heart stopped. Lord Krishna sitting in my living room, not in a frame. I was still dreaming. I hadn't awakened. Lord Krishna picked up a little figurine of Lord Ganesha sitting on my desk, inspected it and said, "Not bad, the detail is pretty accurate". I seemed to be cognisant. This seemed a lot like real life.

"Buying scrap iron old battery buying". "Huh?" Premchand, the neighbourhood Bob-the-Builder, blew his horn and yelled from the road that he was passing back later to fix the pump. The dogs were also doing their usual greeting of the post lady. This felt like very real life. But how could it be? Because back at the farm, Lord Krishna was in my living room. I walked back to the office area and sure enough there sat the enigmatic Lord Krishna, flute in hand, in majestic presence. I couldn't speak, and if I could have, what did one say to the Lord of the universe, "coffee? Tea? My Lordship?

Lord Krishna smiled and walked through the doors into the yard space and into the ether. I jotted down these words that seemed to have been saturating my mind at the time, but didn't come from me. I felt like a telephone cord; I wasn't the conversation in the line, just the transmitter.

"The moment you start feeling abundant and worthy you start generating your wealth; the moment you start feeling whole your healing begins. The moment you start feeling empowered you are closer to your success; your thinking and feeling is changing the outcomes. It was the difference between living as a victim in your world and being a divine creator. Love yourself and all of life. You are not in the universe; the universe is in you. Practice what you want to become"!

Tropical Storm Warning in Sweet Sweet TnT

W ell, yes! Trinis eh easy nah. No body take on the meteorological office orange alert. For two days now they are clambering about the US hurricane helicopter and what the predictions would be for Bonnie. Is only when KFC send out via all media that ALL THEIR LOCATIONS WOULD BE CLOSING AT six pm, then Trinsi realise, ting serious!

The closure of KFC, that is a national crisis!

So, we in grocery, playing tag team with other patrons, holding space in the line while trolleys get filled on a tag team basis. I had to decide whether we eating chicken or chips ahoy, because it was the same price. Thank God we don't really like chocolate, so the chunky priced at $65 didn't bother me.

I also realized all the familiar brands disappearing one by one, the household brand ramen soup; the Keebler cookies; real ting was missing, even before Bonnie. It was unsettling.

But the worse one yet! One pomegranate for $87. I silently wondered if them wanted 87 kicks!

So, we buy the bread at the 33.3% increase. Several loaves, all kind of bread! Some people even buy a 'cracker' in preparation for the power outages! Not me. God make hot dog and my mother was the sandwich queen!

The children had mixed emotions. That is misrepresentation, my daughter was the only child who was maddened by the closure of schools as she needed to finish the end of year exam!

We wait; we wait; we went for a storm run. We eh see nutting resembling a storm.

Trini prepare for storm though, rum, cards, and a duck!

But nutin!

We out for duck!

We get a slight drizzle; slight, no jones.

Gusty winds? Where? Which part? Yuh could tell me? The Caroni River sailing smoothly at barely half mass.

It looks like the storm loss or Bonnie find Clyde and say 'rain check'. Or it was brewing in a teacup? Either way, it miss we or it pass between we, because everything in perfect order. The roads clear! If is one thing Trini know, is how to prepare for aftermaths. So, everybody still under their blankets, waiting for storm, while the roads dry dry and clear. "I happy happy happy, I more than happy", said the late Blaxx. But he damn right, and I agree with him. Because Kess say "I am blessed yes, I never fete more, never less, like Lavantille I fill ah success … for them sucker them ah bring cockset". He knows!

In Trini we does leave stress and worries for important issues; when does wine and jam season resume? Why was KFC closing all locations and not just some?

We bless yes! Kess was right.

Anyway, after all this excitement it have more excitement to come; where is our Prime Minister? Is he also facing the same sentence as our neighbouring Jamaican Prime Minister?

But while we Trinis know all the headlines; the interest is where is the storm after party? Because de party cyah done without a lil wine and jam. Is fête before, during, and after the storm, even if it didn't have a storm. That's how we are; focused! We doh play wit dat!

But it's a vibe - yuh either get it or you don't. We have our own way of doing life. Is a wonder why tens of thousands come here to see what is referred to as, the greatest show on earth. Cause we know how to do it!

Another one for the books yes —- Jesus? Let me see yuh id. Nazareth!? Nah! Nah! I ent taking no chain up this time! Bonnie was seen stuck in traffic at the price plaza round about!

Of Man And Flesh

"This is too much stimulation", he said. "I have never received that as feedback, but ok. I'm sure honesty has a place, but it's not on my bed at the moment".

"I did not mean that in a bad way, at all", he said. His mouth consumed in a smile that extended to touch my heart chakra. Because five minutes ago this exchange would have seemed like the first thing you realise while on a hike, that it was a mistake!

Let's open our experience to the 5th dimension by using the intensity of the stimulation to elevate our consciousness. I laughed and agreed this should stay in my thought realm.

This man's skin was enough to open portals in my mind. Smooth and silky knew nothing of this dimension. It beckoned your attention and kept you entranced in its undulating rising and falling into the mists of beauty, seen and unseen. This is what the bible called of the flesh. That to partake of its pleasure was to sit with Lucy in the Sky with Diamonds.

We had agreed, or rather I had stipulated, one hour, then a drive. If he had it his way, it would be a one-hour drive, then sleep. Reluctantly, he agreed to my proposition.

"I am not in that mind space, ok?"

"Dude, I just want to lie down. Rest, be still for a moment, with you, a bonus". I finished folding the laundry, he gave his two cents about that too, always suggesting to me how to make my life more manageable.

"So, this is fun for you?'

"Not fun, but I don't mind."

"Would you rather do it or not?"

"Not! Obviously, it's laundry not a martini!"

With my whole body resting on his chest, I was fully satiated. Grounded and still. Breathing him in on his exhale and him breathing me in on mine. The beauty of oneness lies in synchronicity of flow, no separation, one breath, one movement, in and out. It wasn't my breath or his, it was breath, with all its rhythmic interchange. Breathing made two become one.

We were content to lie in each other, but my hands, like a moth to a flame, started to caress his bare skin. The mould of his shoulder filled my palm, what I could not hold in, slipped into my skin, coursed through my veins, and emptied in my heart.

"We would see snake, raccoon, crocodile real thing because of the rain, I told you drive first, cause how to get up from the mystery of this vortex remains unsolved".

I raised my head from his waistline, my curls cascading all down his torso. His body lay motionless, almost asleep. I caressed my body against his. First my face on along the side of his pelvis, then up to his chest, through to his neck, twisting my body as his contoured underneath mine. I was happy to bask in him. My hands were roaming freely along his inner thighs, beckoning them to play a little. But then his face turned to meet mine, mouth opened. He took my breath and held my movement still. My body was locked with my face in his hands.

A tropical storm was what the meteorological office promised. There had been no sign of this until now. The downpour beating the roof seemed to galvanise our bodies tighter together. Gusty winds moved trees, roof tops, but our bodies were rigidly held together. The rivers burst its banks and so did we.

I am reminded of the words of Maya Angelou, "If you need permission to go, I liberate you. Love liberates, it does not bind."

Pablo Neruda said it perfectly, "I love you as certain dark things are to be loved…"

Today you gave me some of you. You made me radioactive; like electricity charging through my body, one touch and I was ignited.

Nurturing each other always into new possibilities. Never putting each other into straitjackets of judgment and opinions. It was nourishing all round.

Registering A Death In Trinidad And Tobago

When you going to register a death in Trinidad, walk with tings to pitch a tent, canned foods, and a flashlight. Vanessa Williams sang 'bout a whole new world, it's not here in sweet, sweet TnT, for we have a different set of rules. One for living, the other for surviving, not survival of the 1% eh!; dem business fix, now and in the hereafter for generations to come.

Take for instance the security guards at the district medical office for Caroni. If they give you a form that the nice people from Dass Funeral home filled for you, because them is class and they know you grief stricken and can't focus on the deceased yet as body. Because you now leave them in Mt. Hope ward three Cardiology, so they take the burden off and make life a little easy and fill out the form for you, dem security guards? Well dey not having it!

"I give you a form."

"No, I got this at Dass."

"This is not the form I now give you."

"But it is the same form; same information."

"Where de the form I now give you"?

"Fill that one! De funeral home not supposed to have that!"

And so, realising I was up against a system that is designed to help you with low blood pressure and perfect some of the beatitude they spoke about in 'Convant', like patience and humility, I walked away with the form she just gave me with a renewed sense of opportunity.

I wanted to consult with my uncle Barry as to how preposterous this scenario presented, but the silencing I was met with is engulfing. I knew he would shake his head and smile, trying to communicate to me the wisdom he had about things I would never understand.

So, to get the ordeal sorted out as quickly as possible and following instructions on the sign on the door, I knocked once and awaited my fate. The security guard peeped out.

"Excuse me, how long again?" I said, as I wanted to kill a few birds with the time I had, or had not.

"We not ready for you yet."

So, I resigned that I was powerless in the fight to expedite anything at that moment.

Also remember to walk with a friend. You might pass away, but the process lives on.

In Trinidad, when yuh see a majestic macaw in a cage, it's because that's how he loves birds. I see somebody advertise their business as exploring the wild islands of Trinidad and Tobago, they must be right. Cause is not just mapepire waiting to bite and cripple yuh ass, but the mapepire of existence living right next to you.

No progress, traffic jam in yuh cunt, and sleepless chirren going to school expecting to bring home ah education in a book bag full of bricks! We not only wrong side, we upside dong and inside out.

The level of inefficiency was suffocating, but that was how the regular average con man likes it. Cause he always know a man who could put things in place at a cost. Lord Fadda! And no body locking up the grocery owners?! Them is the only ones laughing all the way to the bank. Fuck the farmers. The informal economy is what keeping this lil island afloat. The middle income, honest earning, tax paying citizens. The same ones, who, because of the education their fathers and forefathers sacrificed, they *jahaji* bundle for, is now, unqualified for a home grant, or education grant, or food grant. Because yuh over the education bracket to afford you a grant to live. Because the government of the day, squandering like come see never see, and not diversifying the economy. No economic activity, no investment. And unemployment on the rise. Doh forget what Covid do to the small and medium business owners. The government of the day should not only be investigated for the Petrotrin pipeline murders, four they killed in a pipeline. And the rest of we? They are killing us slowly by their misfeasance in public office and gross mis management of every resource we ever had. While some living it up on grants, on account of their lazy, non-ambitious, always pregnant, zest, selling sweetie in a bottle by the side of the road.

It different out here. Everyone learns about a fair opportunity and a system based on meritocracy. Here? Papa, I tell you. Is not what yuh know, is who yuh know, and who know you! And if they don't know you, well crapaud smoke yuh pipe, because is your chile Secondary Entrance Assessment (SEA) marks they switch with somebody dey know, to send dem fren and family to dem first choice.

We are reeking of shit in this place! But for a *juzzie*, wine and jam with a music truck and more handouts, pelting ting from de truck, election results prove dat we like it so!

So don't criticise me when I say I love this country, but I am getting my chirren away from this toxic environment. The toxicity is when, like me, I remain here, thinking I could make ah difference, make a change, make this place the beautiful island I know it to be in my heart and soul. Then the reality that presents itself, is one whey you realise yuh can't change this system, because you not of the system, and you marginalized. Hopes marginalized; happiness marginalized, the dream of making the difference is shit sure marginalized.

Is my whole family abandon this country, because dem see the light? Me? I was so blind I was dotish. So, I here trying to register the death of my uncle Barry, alone, because the family from away have to make arrangements to come dong for the funeral I trying to arrange. But this security guard not making it easy, because of a form. She has the backing of a whole system colonised and engineered to make this process the most disgusting experience for the living yet. I so numb, I don't think I even get to reconcile with what I doing here. Fuss I vex.

That is the Gramoxone we are forced to sip, each day as we sit imprisoned in our cars, trying to get to work, to make a dollar, to spend in gas, to eat butter and roti.

Santimanitay!

The Great Escape!

⌢⌣⌢

I saw him glide aboard his 54-feet yacht with his million-dollar smile.

The black Ray Ban rested on his perfect facial bone structure. His skin was the milk chocolate brown I dreamed to lick off one day. His black brushed-back hair, neatly parted to the side with surgical precision, daring to not risk any movement while he captained the vessel and cavorted about taking charge of everything and everyone on board.

He glanced in my direction with a familiar enough nod, shrouded in mystery and dripping sex appeal. What were the thoughts he thought? That damn beard would be to my demise one day!

I had known him for years, sat opposite him in meetings while dispensing legal advice to his parents on land transactions and on their company's legal obligations per corporate commercial compliance, among other things.

So polite with executional manners. His staff could have offered and brought the tea, but instead, he did it. We maintained professionalism and more than common courtesy, his courtesy was anything but common. A more refined specimen didn't exist. He was distinction standing at 6ft. tall, polished, and smooth!

Now sitting before him around the company's conference table, together with his parents, all I could feel were his hands on my legs, and his hot shorts breaths on my neck. With the daze of the night in the background, and the wind blowing freely under my dress prompted by his urgency to caress my body, I forgot where I was.

"Ms. Jadoonanan, are you with us?" I was floating aboard the SS. Gone Astray. I hadn't heard the questions nor the discussion. My point of reference was his cologne and where it propelled me. Sometimes I thought he did it on purpose. You must know how gorgeous you are and to top it off, with a scent that was sex in a bottle, he was just showing off now! But he wasn't! The damn man walked with humility, amidst all the power he managed to be very down to earth, with great fashion sense!

I was cascading down the rabbit hole, legs, skin, touch. I could only recount with clarity the smoothness of his skin — all of it!

Empty silence filled the room. What had I missed? Think quick!

"I am sorry, I must be excused. I am expected at a virtual injunction hearing, for which the judge has decided, on short notice, that she will hear our ex-parte application, at 2:30". I glanced at my phone to give the alibi for my daydreaming, credibility. It was 2:20. My exit was imminent. I managed to stave off embarrassment for one day with my dignity intact. Hopefully.

I had followed him up the deck, not in a stalking kind of way, but very similar.

I had hoped that we might have had a few laughs and enjoy the music. Given the gorgeous ambiance of the night's sky, I got the courage to muster up the nerve to at least present myself for the opportunity. The ocean had other plans for me. Earlier that evening, we were on the deck taking goofy photos and clowning around with some of the other guests. It was like that when you have reckless abandon and put chance in the next drink after the next drink.

God knew how he took away chunks of the night —he had to! Next thing I remembered, he was up against me. I could feel him. Close to my skin, my neck. Oh, and the memory of those hands up and down my legs! He was enjoying the feel of my body and with the feedback of reciprocity of the intensity of the happening, 'cause it was happening. This moment I had imagined for years was happening, and it was better than my imagination could conjure.

We were intwined in each other, I didn't know when the others left. The rhythm of the night, the open air, the cloud of "all is well and right as rain", enveloped my thoughts and lifted me straight from the reality I knew and cast me as the lead role in "whose life is this any way"?

I was happy to watch, but after the instructions, "my room is down the hall, first door on the left". I was reminded that this was not a spectator sport, and the role required my input. This was the theatre, and tonight was show time. No time to perfect the imperfected, no second zees, no rehearsing. No directing, no spectating. Action!

"Would you like a cup of tea Ms. Jadoonanan?"

"Yes, thank you," I managed without delay.

What I really needed was a stiff one! _A drink! A stiff drink! My mind was drifting off into the abyss already. How do I steer it back? This was not the time or place to lose presence. He was there again. And commanded the room's full attention effortlessly, fully garbed in traditional Islamic wear. Even in grief, this man exuded pure arresting, unsolicited appeal. He was attending to family members, guests who had come to pay their respects, formalities of the ceremony and the overall administration of the event; his grandmother's funeral. All this with the ease of control and command that he wore naturally, like his smile. In white, he was more striking than lightning. Lightning, if it did strike, was 'gonna' be on my account, aimed at my misplaced lascivious thoughts. This man was no good. I would go straight to hell.

"I'm sorry for your loss, please accept my deepest". I could see them now, Jesus, Allah and Krishna, all shaking their heads in quiet derision of my thoughts. I was sorry! The tenderest hug exchange, followed by a nice platonic shoulder squeeze was my petition for absolution.

I followed the instructions and sure enough there was a bed. He opened the door and was over me in seconds. He was so gorgeous. Even in the dark I could feel his beauty. His face so close to mine, calling my name, Melissa? Melissa? I wanted to answer but I was enthralled in the magic of his gaze and the strength of his hands on my body. Melissa?

I opened my eyes and he was close to my lips; I opened my mouth in readiness for the thrilling evening that awaited me.

"She's awake!

Wtf! Why was everyone cheering and worse yet, in the room, with us, on the bed?

"Apparently, as the boat set sail, the fumes from the exhaust knocked you out. You fainted on the steps to the cabin. I carried you to my room. I awaited your regaining consciousness. I was a paramedic a long time ago."

Of course you were!

I lay motionless, couldn't have been long until I could try to piece together the ensemble of events in my head that didn't match the evidence before me.

"And the photos on the deck…. I almost forgot we did that."

"Sorry, what photos?"

Now that I was conscious, I wasn't sure that I wanted to be. I wanted to go back to that place, to the moment where we were about to kiss. About to touch that smile with mine. Before I was dying with anticipation, now I was just dying of embarrassment! What was real? Any of it? Only he knew.

This was definitely entry level into hell.

About the Author

MELISSA JADOONANAN is an attorney at law by profession, a sister, a daughter, a friend and the creative director of her life. She has worked widely, by virtue of being mother, in the fields of chauffeuring; chefing; caretaking; finance managing. She is not an open water swimmer, or any kind of, not an Olympic winner, of even close. Hasn't climbed mount Everest, but hopes to! She is a dog lover but has been told she is not. She is an ordinary person with an odd perspective for calling a thing a thing. She lives with her two wonderful children in Trinidad with their two dogs!

Lightning Source UK Ltd.
Milton Keynes UK
UKHW040748260123
416002UK00001B/2